SPOTLIGHT ON BLENDS

Book One
Initial
Consonant Blends

Book One
Initial
Consonant Blends

First edition published by The Robinswood Press 1997

© Gillian Aitken 1997, 1999, 2003

Gillian Aitken has asserted her right under the Copyright, Designs
and Patents Act 1988 to be identified as the author of this work.

Designed by Steve Emms

The Robinswood Press

Stourbridge England

ISBN 1-869981-553

CONTENTS

ABOUT THE AUTHOR

Gillian Aitken MA, PGCE, RSA Dip. TEFLA, AMBDA, Dip. Psych. (Open)

Gillian Aitken trained originally as an English teacher and taught in schools for a number of years. More recently, she has concentrated on areas in teaching English where a specialised approach is required. These have included teaching English to pupils with Special Educational Needs, teaching pupils where English is a Second or Foreign Language, and adult literacy work with the Dyslexia Institute.

Ms Aitken therefore has a unique range of experience gained practically both in Britain and abroad, and through further academic study. This background has provided her with both a clear understanding of the challenges faced by teachers in a variety of different situations and also perfect opportunities to develop a range of exercises – such as the blend exercises in both these *"Spotlight on Blends"* titles, the Wordsearch exercises in the *"Spotlight on Words"* books, and the exercises in the two *"Spotlight on Suffixes"* titles. All these exercises meet the educationalist's requirement to build spelling and reading skills whilst the pupil becomes engrossed in the challenge and enjoyment of the exercises themselves.

Ms Aitken lives in Sussex and continues to work as a specialist English teacher. She is an Associate Member of the British Dyslexia Association and a Graduate Member of the British Psychological Society.

FOREWORD

Like most busy enthusiastic teachers, I am always interested to see what new resource material is available to help those pupils who require extra attention for specific difficulties. Gillian Aitken's first book *"Spotlight on Words"* has proved very popular with my students and has provided an enjoyable way of reinforcing phonic sounds in a user-friendly format. The pupils are having fun while working on a particular area that requires additional strengthening.

The criteria that are particularly important to me in selecting resource material are:

- good, clear print.
- an uncluttered layout.
- variety.
- a high interest level without being gimmicky.
- work that is challenging but not too daunting.
- worksheets that cover just one specific point for use alongside a structured teaching programme.
- work that has a high interest level for older pupils too.
- clear guidelines on how to use the resources.

Gillian Aitken's latest contribution *"Spotlight on Blends"* again meets these criteria. It will therefore be a valuable addition to the resource material for both the specialist and class teacher to use alongside material already available and to provide reinforcement of sounds already taught and skills such as scanning, tracking and visual discrimination.

Pat Denham
SEN Teacher Elmfield Steiner School and VI Specialist Teacher with Sandwell MBC.

Pat Denham, BPhil, Cert Ed, is a teacher with extensive teaching experience in both the State and independent sectors and across a wide age range of pupils. Her work includes Class Teaching in a Steiner school and Special Needs teaching, especially for visually impaired pupils, throughout the educational spectrum.

INTRODUCTION

"Spotlight on Blends" – *Book One* – aims to give systematic practice of consonant blends at the beginning of words, while *Book Two* (published as a separate book) focuses on end blends. Such blends are an essential part of our spelling system. Their high frequency means that they should be an integral part of any structured literacy programme, especially in the earlier stages, while for dyslexic pupils they need constant practice and reinforcement both for reading and spelling. Younger pupils who are learning to read and write, even if they do not have a specific learning difficulty, also need training in the use of consonant blends. The worksheets contained in *"Spotlight on Blends"* – *Book One* and *Book Two* – are thus intended as a useful resource for the busy teacher following a phonic approach to teach reading and spelling. The order in which the worksheets are used will depend entirely on the structured programme which the teacher is following, and the individual needs of each pupil.

Although some attention is given to blends in existing materials aimed primarily at younger pupils in the early stages of reading and spelling, practice exercises tend to be limited in scope, often requiring the child to match the initial blend to a picture. Blends of various kinds tend to be taught together rather than differentiated. The material in *"Spotlight on Blends"* aims for a more systematic approach to the teaching of consonant blends. *Book One,* for example, starts with blends made with 's' such as 'st' and 'sp', then covers those made with 'r' and 'l', and gives separate practice of the more difficult three-consonant blends such as 'spr' and 'str'. If a blend can be used in both initial and final position such as 'st' or 'sk', it will appear in *Book One* and *Book Two.*

For many blends (for example, 'sm' and 'sn'), practice is given at two levels. The lower level will use words which have mainly short vowels and simple patterns, while the higher level will employ words containing long vowels and a greater variety of phonic patterns including two-syllable words. The Level One worksheets are thus suitable for pupils who have had little or no exposure to the target blends and who are at the early stages of decoding, while the Level Two worksheets allow the teacher to consolidate these sounds at a later stage.

For pupils whose reading skills are considerably in advance of their spelling skills, the Level Two worksheets should provide necessary practice of the target blends without using childish or simplistic worksheets aimed at much younger pupils. The material in *"Spotlight on Blends"* is generally suitable for pupils of 7 years or above, and many of the worksheets would be appropriate for secondary aged pupils or adults. The worksheets are varied in format but aim for clarity and an uncluttered visual layout so that the pupil can see at a glance what to do.

Tasks are of different kinds. However, the main emphasis is on sound blending and most of the exercises are designed to raise awareness of regular and predictable sound combinations concerning consonant blends. Current research has highlighted the importance of phonological processing in learning to read and spell, and it is this deficit which is seen as the core of the dyslexic's difficulties with language. Indeed, the Orton Dyslexia Society recently adopted a revised definition of dyslexia in recognition of the growing international agreement among researchers of the hypothesis regarding inefficient phonological processing. *"Dyslexia is a specific and language-based disorder of constitutional origin, characterised by difficulties in single word decoding, usually reflecting insufficient phonological processing abilities."* (Orton Dyslexia Society, 1994.) Indeed, phonological awareness is crucial to any young child learning to read and write, and this belief is now endorsed in National Curriculum guidelines which stipulate that pupils in the earlier stages of spelling must be taught to *"recognise, and use correctly, regular patterns for vowel sounds and common letter shapes"*. For the dyslexic pupil, thorough and systematic training in sound processing and sound/symbol correlation provide the only route to literacy.

Phonological processing operates on different levels. The pupil must first be able to distinguish individual sounds. Consonant blends contain two elements of sound, but individual units of sound or phonemes are altered when combined in this way. Thus, the phoneme /p/ is strongly aspirated (that is, pronounced with a puff of air) when found at the beginning of an accented syllable and before a vowel, and to a lesser extent at the end of a word. However, when combined with /s/ in the blend 'sp', this aspiration is largely lost and the sound is actually more like 'sb'. Thus, although a child can cope with individual phonemes, it does not follow that s/he will be able to combine the same phonemes into blends or clusters. This is why separate and systematic practice is needed. The sound combination should be linked directly to the string of letters which represents this sound by asking the pupil to say the sound before s/he writes the blend (preferably in cursive writing), and naming the letters while writing the blend.

Many of the blends are introduced contrastively, for example, 'st' is contrasted with 'sp', and 'sm' with 'sn', because of similarities in sound. For pupils with severe sound processing difficulties, each blend should be practised separately before being contrasted with a similar sound. It might be advisable to do some basic sound discrimination practice before beginning each worksheet to ensure that the pupil can identify the target sound. Many of the worksheets incorporate practice of blending the beginning of the word ('onset') with the remaining chunk ('rime'), or vice-versa. In *Book One* of *"Spotlight on Blends",* the onset will, of course, consist of the initial consonant blend which is being focused on. However, the necessity to choose the correct rime will give incidental practice of many other phonic patterns, thus reinforcing other sound/symbol correlations.

Other exercises involve the correct identification of the medial vowel sound, or the ability to distinguish between real and nonsense words. A pupil faced with a nonsense word is forced to decode phonetically, and cannot process the word visually. More advanced sound blending exercises involve the blending of Beginning, Middle and End sounds to make as many words as possible with a given combination of sounds (for example, Worksheets 40a and 40b).

The work of researchers like Peter Bryant and Lynette Bradley has highlighted the importance of rhyme recognition in phonological training. This means teaching the child to identify rhyming patterns both in sound and corresponding visual letter strings, and thus forging connections between sound and symbol which were not previously made.

Identification of rhyming patterns can be practised in a variety of ways, including games like rhyming Bingo. In *Book One* of *"Spotlight on Blends"*, there are four worksheets (numbers 17, 18, 36 and 37) which require the pupil to identify a rhyming word in a line of letters and then to think of further rhyming words.

While the focus in the worksheets is thus on sound awareness and sound blending as described above, endeavour has also been made to incorporate target words in a meaningful linguistic context. Thus, there are many gap-filling exercises which encourage the pupil to use contextual clues in order to make the correct selection, an exercise which develops reading comprehension and thinking skills. Other exercises require the child to match words with the correct definition.

Dyslexic pupils with reading problems often have a limited vocabulary, and the Level Two worksheets deliberately aim to extend knowledge of word meanings by the inclusion of one or two less common words. Some help might thus be necessary in the more difficult gap-filling exercises. The pupil should also be encouraged to use a dictionary or spell-checker if s/he is not sure of possible sound combinations in the blending exercises. In two worksheets (numbers 4 and 29) the pupils are encouraged to write sentences of their own using the target words. Teachers can, of course, follow up any of the worksheets by a similar exercise.

It is recognised that consonant blends cause visual sequencing difficulties as well as auditory ones, and therefore some specific Visual Discrimination Practice worksheets have been included (for example, number 14 for 'br' and 'dr', and number 35 for mixed 'l' blends which are often mis-read). Two wordsearches have also been included (numbers 3 and 41) which give practice in visual discrimination and provide a diverting change from the more usual format.

As many of the worksheets contrast two or more blends, it is suggested that different coloured pens are used for writing each blend, in order to highlight this contrast. This would be particularly relevant in exercises where the correct initial blend has to be chosen in order to complete the word, for example, the first exercises in Worksheets 1 and 2.

Initial consonant blends fall within three main categories – those beginning with /s/ as the first element such as 'st' or 'sp'; those which have /r/ as the second element, such as 'pr' or 'tr'; and those which blend with /l/ such as 'cl' or 'pl'. The worksheets give extensive practice of each blend, at first narrowly contrasted with just one or two other blends, and then in a mixed blend exercise. The 'r' blends are the most frequent, and are therefore practised in different combinations. Thus, 'cr' is contrasted with 'br' and 'tr' in Worksheets 10 and 11, but with 'fr' and 'gr' in Worksheet 20.

The blend 'fr' is introduced in isolation (Worksheets 15 and 16) before it is contrasted, because this is a difficult sound to distinguish and pronounce. As 'fr' is often confused with 'thr', Worksheet number 25 gives specific practice in discriminating these two sounds. The three-consonant blends 'scr', 'str' and 'spr' are given separate treatment at two levels of difficulty (Worksheets 26 and 27). Initial blends with 'l' cause fewer auditory problems, and so there are not quite so many practice sheets as for the 'r' blends. The blend 'sl' appears with the other 'l' blends, not with the 's' blending words. The last two worksheets contrast 'r' and 'l' blends in pairs such as 'gr' / 'gl', 'fr' / 'fl', and so on.

Detailed teaching notes to accompany each worksheet are to be found in the rear section of the book after the worksheets (pages 56 to 70). These include suggestions about using the worksheets, and highlight possible areas of difficulty where the pupil might need guidance, or where ambiguity might arise.

Answers are included where appropriate. Phonetic symbols have not been used to describe sounds in the teaching notes as it is assumed that most teachers will not be familiar with these symbols. A sound is represented by the letter names inside slanted brackets, for example, /st/, while a spelling choice is indicated by inverted commas, such as 'st'. Long vowel sounds are indicated by the diacritic /¯/ above the vowel, for example, /ū/ as in 'flūid', while short vowel sounds are indicated by the diacritic /˘/ above the vowel, such as /ă/, as in 'flăt'.

Gillian Aitken

Blends: st sp

Each word below begins with (st) or (sp).
Choose the correct blend to start each word.

__in	__amp	__and	__ot
__end	__ell	__op	__it
__ep	__uck	__at	__ing

Write each word in the correct list below.

st   sp

_____   _____   _____   _____

_____   _____   _____   _____

_____   _____   _____   _____

Now choose a (st) or (sp) word to finish each sentence.
(You don't have to use all the words.)

1 Tom got _____ in the lift.

2 The bus is not going to _____ .

3 Pam can read and _____ very well.

4 Can an ant _____ you?

5 It is not good manners to _____ .

6 Jack will _____ his holiday in Scotland.

Blends: st sp

Each word below begins with (st) or (sp).
Choose the correct blend to start each word.

__one	__anner	__ine	__ag
__amp	__ade	__eep	__elt
__ite	__udent	__arks	__eal
__eech	__ider	__ammer	__ack

Write each word in the correct list below.

st   **sp**

_____ _____   _____ _____

_____ _____   _____ _____

_____ _____   _____ _____

_____ _____   _____ _____

Now choose a (st) or (sp) word from the above lists
to finish each sentence.
(You don't have to use all the words.)

1 A _____ is useful if you need to mend your car.

2 _____ from the fire fell on to the carpet.

3 The angry child _____ed his feet.

4 The old car could not get up the _____ hill.

5 The _____ went to his class in _____ of
having a bad cold.

6 When the best man stood up to give his _____,
he was so nervous that he started to _____.

Blends:

Make a REAL word by choosing the correct ending.

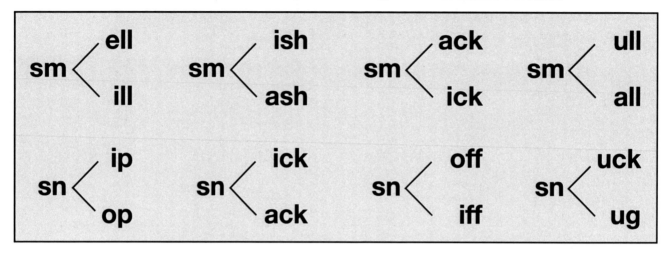

Now find the 8 REAL words in the wordsearch below.
Write each word on the lines beside the square.
(Words go ACROSS or DOWN only.)

k	c	s	m	a	s	h	n
s	i	m	z	s	n	u	g
n	s	l	a	o	f	t	s
a	m	s	m	a	l	l	n
c	e	y	e	z	b	d	i
k	l	s	n	i	p	j	f
r	l	p	g	u	q	v	f
h	x	s	m	a	c	k	w

_____

_____

_____

_____

_____

_____

_____

_____

Choose (sm) or (sn) to finish the words in these sentences.

1   Tom's grandad ___okes a pipe.

2   A ___ail has a shell on its back.

3   A baby's skin is very ___ooth.

4   Would you like to keep a ___ake as a pet?

5   I think I am going to ___eeze.

6   You ___ile if you feel happy.

Blends: sm   sn

Make a REAL word by choosing the correct ending.

(Note that both endings can be used in several cases.)

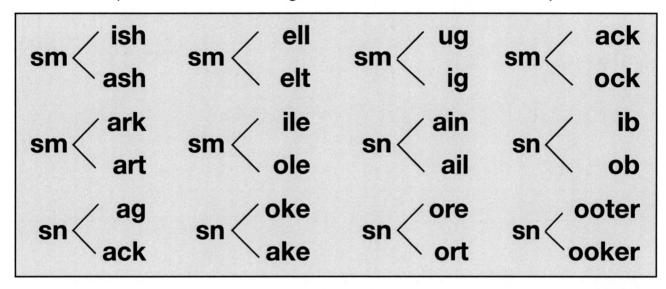

Now write out the words you have made in the correct list. You should have 8 words beginning with sm and 8 words beginning with sn.

sm   ### sn

_____ _____ _____   _____ _____ _____

_____ _____ _____   _____ _____ _____

_____ _____   _____ _____

Write 3 sentences on the lines below using some of the above words. Can you use 2 words in one sentence?

_____

_____

_____

_____

_____

_____

Can you read the sm and sn words below?

smother	snorkel	snigger	smudge
sneaker	snare	smuggle	snatch
	smarten	smallpox	

Now you have read the words, how many can you remember without looking?

_____

Blends: | st | sp | sn | sm |

Circle the 6 nonsense words and put them in the bin.

stop	spop	snap	stick
spag	smash	stamp	steg
smell	snup	stem	stin
spin	stiff	small	smab

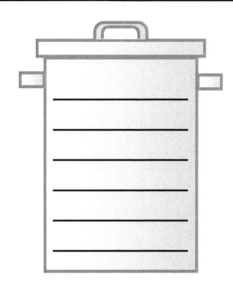

**Now choose the correct blend st sp sn or sm
to complete each word in the sentences below.**

1 The ___all boy held his mother's hand.

2 A top can ___in.

3 If you drop that glass dish, it will ___ash.

4 Can you play ___ap?

5 How much did you ___end in the shops?

6 Have you got a ___amp for my letter?

7 Ben was ___anding on the top ___ep of the ladder.

8 I can't ___op ___iffing because of my cold.

Blends: | st | sp | sn | sm |

**Tick the words which are REAL words. Put a
cross by the words which are NOT real words.**

stool	snout	spand	snowy	spike
smank	spare	stencil	steamy	stell
sneak	stang	snobbish	spelt	stairs
smuck	spine	stutter	spinter	stupid

**Now choose (st) (sp) (sn) or (sm) to
complete each word in the sentences below.**

(You will not find the words in the box above.)

1 Mr. ___ith ___ent all morning ___uck in the lift!

2 Susan felt very ___ug after she had ___uggled down
under the warm blankets.

3 We could see the church ___eeple when we ___ood
on the top ___ep of the wooden ___ile.

4 A ___irk is a silly ___ile, and a ___igger is an unkind
laugh.

5 The gardener ___opped digging when his ___ade hit
a sharp ___one.

6 If you are swimming underwater with a ___orkel, it is
very difficult to ___eak!

7 The ___oke from all the factory chimneys caused a
thick ___og to lie all over the town.

8 The dust which Jane inhaled made her ___eeze
and ___iff.

Blends: | sk | | sc |

The words _'Scotland'_ and _'skip'_ both begin with the same sound. What is it? What are the 2 ways of spelling this sound?

| _____ | | _____ |

Rule:

At the beginning of words, use (sk) before 'i', 'y' and 'e'.

_____in	_____etch	_____ip
_____eleton	_____im	_____ewer
_____id	_____ill	_____y

Use (sc) before 'a', 'o' or 'u'.

____ab	____otland	____um
____ar	____otch	____uffle
____an	____oop	____urry
____amper	____ore	____ulpture
____are	____orch	____ulptor
____atter	____out	

Rule Breakers!

Note the following 3 words beginning with (sk) which break the rule. Use each word in the sentence below.

skate   skunk   skull

The _____ cracked his _____ when he tried to _____ on the frozen lake!

Blends: | sk | | sc |

**Choose the correct blend to begin each
word below. Watch out for the 3 rule breakers!**

___im   ___ore   ___urry   ___y   ___ill

___inny   ___um   ___ate   ___ore   ___uffle

___amper   ___unk   ___otch   ___atter

___ulpture   ___etch   ___oop   ___eleton

Find words from the above list to match the meanings below.

1   To draw the outline of something.   _ _ _ _ _ _

2   To run quickly like a small animal.   _ _ _ _ _ _ _ _

3   A struggle or short fight.   _ _ _ _ _ _ _ _

4   Art-form which involves carving in stone.   _ _ _ _ _ _ _ _ _

5   Bone framework of the human body.   _ _ _ _ _ _ _ _

6   To throw or put here and there.   _ _ _ _ _ _ _

**The spelling rule also works in the middle of a word,
at the beginning of a syllable with the hard 'k' sound.**

For example: es/cort   bas/ket

Divide the words below into syllables in the same way.

r a s c a l   b r i s k e t

e s c a l a t o r   m u s k e t

d e s c a n t   g a s k e t

m a s c o t   c a s k e t

Blend:

Find 10 words beginning with (squ) in the wordsearch.
Then match each word to the definitions below.
(Words go ACROSS and DOWN only.)

h	s	q	u	i	r	t	c	g
s	q	u	i	r	r	e	l	s
q	u	s	q	u	e	a	k	q
u	e	q	r	s	y	k	a	u
i	l	u	s	q	u	i	d	i
g	c	e	v	u	k	o	q	n
g	h	a	d	a	f	b	w	t
l	z	l	j	r	p	s	h	e
e	s	q	u	e	e	z	e	n

1 A small animal.   _ _ _ _ _ _ _ _

2 You do this to a lemon to get the juice out. _ _ _ _ _ _ _ _

3 A four-sided shape.   _ _ _ _ _ _

4 Noise made by a mouse.   _ _ _ _ _ _

5 To force out liquid in a thin stream or jet. _ _ _ _ _ _

6 To look sideways with half-shut eyes.   _ _ _ _ _ _

7 To make a sucking sound – for example,
   when walking through sticky mud.   _ _ _ _ _ _ _ _

8 A cry of pain or fear.   _ _ _ _ _ _

9 A small twisty line or scrawl.   _ _ _ _ _ _ _ _

10 A kind of cuttlefish.   _ _ _ _ _ _

Blend: squa

Read the words below which all start with squa.
Then match each word to the correct meaning.

squat	squash	squander	squall
squalid	squawk	squabble	squad

1 To make a loud, harsh cry (of birds). _____

2 To waste (time or money). _____

3 To sit on one's heels. _____

4 To crush or press flat in a small space. _____

5 A sudden, violent wind, often with rain. _____

6 Dirty, mean, uncared-for. _____

7 A small group – like soldiers – working together. _____

8 To quarrel. _____

Now use each word to fill in the blanks in the sentences below.

1 Brothers and sisters often _____ with each other.

2 The poor family were living in very _____ conditions
   in their tumbledown cottage.

3 A sudden _____ blew off the man's hat.

4 The parrot gave a loud _____ which made us jump.

5 The boy _____ed all his pocket money on sweets
   and comics.

6 A _____ of workmen were sent to repair the road.

7 The tomatoes in the shopping bag got badly _____ed.

8 In our PE lesson we had to _____ on our heels and
   then stand up ten times.

Blends:

Choose (sw)(tw) or (dw) to fill in the blanks in the sentences below.

1   Jim's ___in brother was so much smaller than Jim that he looked like a ___arf in comparison.

2   The boy dropped the ___ig into the river and watched it being ___ept away by the current.

3   The man in the ___eed suit walked with a ___agger, and ___irled and ___eaked his moustache self-importantly.

4   It was hard to believe that the small cottage was the ___elling place for a family of ___elve.

5   There was a ___inkle in the man's eyes after he took another ___ig of whisky!

6   When the child fell off the ___ing, he ___isted his arm which ___elled up badly.

7   The family's supply of ___enty kilos of ___eet potatoes soon began to ___indle as the weeks went by.

Now write out each word beginning with

(sw)(tw) or (dw) in the correct list below.

sw	tw	dw
_____	_____	_____
_____	_____	_____
_____	_____	_____
_____	_____	
_____	_____	
_____	_____	
	_____	
	_____	

Blends: | br | cr | tr |

**Read the words below. Tick the ones which are REAL
words. Put a cross by the words which are NOT real words.**

crop	**brog**	**brick**	**truck**
cress	**trob**	**brop**	**crib**
trap	**crad**	**brush**	**trust**	**trip**
crust	**brat**	**cran**	**track**	**brim**

**Read the words below. Then use each
one to fill in the blanks in the sentences.**

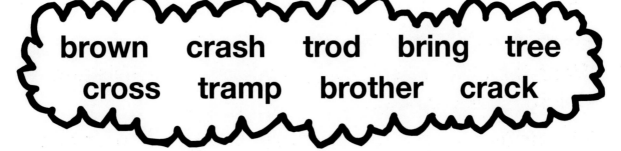

brown   crash   trod   bring   tree

cross   tramp   brother   crack

1   Please _____ me your work so that I can
mark it.

2   The man with the big feet _____ on the child's
left foot in the bus.

3   There was a big _____ in the dish which
Rachel dropped.

4   The _____ liked to sit on the bench in the park.

5   If you stay in the sun, your skin will go _____.

6   The tall _____ fell down in the strong wind
with a loud _____.

7   My _____ was very _____ when I lost
his best pen.

Blends: br cr tr

Read the words below. Tick the ones which are REAL words. Put a cross by the words which are NOT real words.

broken	crisis	trike	credit
brote	brunk	creak	breed
trunpet	crunk	trench	breeze
crimson	tripod	brime	crown
troob	crine	traffic	brass
crape	tray	brandish	

Choose one of the words below to fill in the blanks in the sentences.

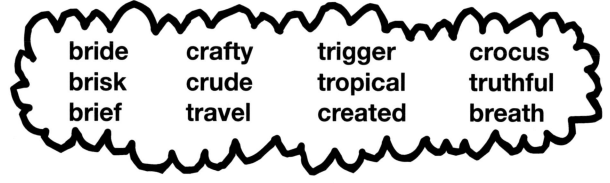

bride	crafty	trigger	crocus
brisk	crude	tropical	truthful
brief	travel	created	breath

1 A _____ is an early spring flower.

2 We were short of _____ after going for a _____ early morning walk to the top of the hill.

3 Oil which has not been refined is called _____ oil.

4 For a few _____ hours on her wedding day the _____ felt like a queen.

5 The bank robber _____ mass panic when he pressed the _____ of his gun.

6 A _____ person is sly and cunning, so is unlikely to be _____.

7 On cold winter days I wish I could _____ by plane to a hot, _____ country!

Blends:  dr gr pr

Join the beginning of each word with the correct ending. Then write out each word on the lines provided.

dr   in   1   *drum*

gr   od   2 _____

pr   um   3 _____

dr   and   4 _____

gr   ick   5 _____

pr   ug   6 _____

dr   een   7 _____

gr   ag   8 _____

Fill in the missing short vowel in the words below.

ă   ĕ   ĭ   ŏ   ŭ

gr__ll	gr__p	pr__nk	gr__b
pr__p	dr__p	dr__ss	pr__m
dr__nk	gr__b	pr__ss	dr__ll

Blends:  dr gr pr

Join the beginning of each word to the correct
ending. Then write out each word on the lines provided.

dr	ace	1	_____
gr	ake	2	_____
pr	ench	3	_____
dr	ave	4	_____
gr	each	5	_____
pr	eam	6	_____
dr	int	7	_____
gr	une	8	_____
pr	eed	9	_____

Fill in the missing vowels in the words
below. Are the vowels long or short?

pr__be	dr__bble	gr__ze	pr__de
gr__m	dr__stic	pr__fit	dr__ft
pr__nk	gr__dge	gr__de	dr__pe
gr__pe	pr__spect	dr__ll	gr__sp

Blends: { br   dr } Visual Discrimination

> **Look carefully to find the word in the box hidden in the line of letters. The number tells you how many times the word is hidden.**

drag	a b r a g d r a g b r a d r a g g	2
brat	b r a t d r a t b r a d b r a t a	2
drip	d r i b b r i p d r i p r d r i p	2
bring	b r i n k d r i n g b r i n g r b	1
drop	p r o p d r o p d r o p b r o p d	2
brown	r d r o w n b r a w n b r o w n d	1
drum	b r d r u d r u m d r u m b r u m	2
bread	b r e d r e a d b r e a d d r e d	1
dry	d r y b r y d r b r y d r y d r y	3
drug	b r d u g d r u g d r u g b r u g	2
brick	b r b i c k d b r i c k b i r c k	1
drink	d r i n k d i r n k d r i n k k i	2
drab	b r a d d r a b d a b d r a b a d	2
bran	b a r n d r a n b r a n d b r a n	2
drill	d i r l d r i l l b r i l l d i r	1

25

Blend: fr

Unscramble the (fr) words below to match the meanings.

g f o r	A small animal which likes water.	_____
r s e f h	Not stale or old.	_____
s o f t r	It comes on cold winter nights.	_____
r f m a e	Something surrounding a picture.	_____
r k n f a	Boy's name, or a word meaning open in thought or feeling.	_____
a f i r l	Weak, not strong.	_____
z e f e r e	To become ice.	_____
g r e d f i	Where you keep butter and milk.	_____
m o f r	Where are you ....?	_____
r i f t u	Bananas, apples, plums...	_____

Do you know these words?

1 A day of the week.   _ _ _ _ _ _

2 To cook in oil or fat.   _ _ _

3 A person you like and spend time with.   _ _ _ _ _ _

4 You don't have to pay if something is: _ _ _ _

5 Opposite of back.   _ _ _ _ _

Test Your Memory

You should have found 15 words beginning with (fr). How many can you remember without looking at the sheet? Give yourself one point for each word you can remember, and one point if the spelling is correct.

Score: Words ☐/15   Spelling ☐/15   Total ☐/30

Blend: fr

Complete each word by adding the initial blend (fr), reading each word as you do so.

___ock   ___ost   ___agment   ___ail

___ank   ___eak   ___eeze   ___olic

___iend   ___uit   ___ill   ___esh

___equent   ___iction   ___ustrate

___iday   ___ugal   ___ontier

Now answer the following questions.

1   To which 3 words can you add suffix 'y' to make a new word?

_____   _____   _____

2   To which word can you add:
    a) suffix 'ship' to make a noun?   _____
    b) suffix 'ness' to make a noun?   _____

3   How many words can take suffix 'ly'?

_____

4   Can you find 4 adjectives in this list?

_____ _____ _____ _____

5   Can you find 2 verbs?   _____ _____

6   Write down all the two-syllable words. Circle the ones which begin with an Open syllable.

_____

_____

Rhyming Words:

br cr dr gr
pr tr fr

In each line of letters find ONE word which rhymes with the word in the box. The word you are looking for must begin with an 'r' blend.

brim	f r a t r i m h s g r a m t o
pram	b r a m t r i m x a g r a m l
crab	o c r j g r u b k e g r a b d
cress	a f c r o s s e d r e s s o t
dry	s o b r y p r a y e t r y u k
grip	b r i g r i t t r a p t r i p
frill	a b r i l l d r i l l h e l l
brick	n q u f r i c k m t r i c k d
tray	w e o f r y a y p r a y i h v
drop	f t r a p c r o p r o d r i p

Write the rhyming pairs below. Can you think of one more word to rhyme with each pair? Write it on the dotted line as in the example.

brim
trim
slim

Rhyming Words:

br cr dr gr pr tr fr

In each line of letters find ONE word which rhymes with the word inside the box. The word you are looking for must begin with an 'r' blend.

grand	t r i b r a n d r a n d e n d a
prank	a q b r a n k i n g d r a n k y
graft	r o b r a f t g v c r a f t u z
frisk	a d r i s b r i s k t r i c k s
grain	j h p r a i n l o d r a i n t y
tribe	a d r i b e b a b e b r i b e h
graze	o y c r a z e f r o z e w g l e
bright	o d r i g h t i g h f r i g h t
crew	u g r o w v f r e w n d r e w n
drone	e b r o m e p r o n e f r o m e

Write 5 rhyming pairs of your choice on the lines below. Can you think of other rhyming words for each pair? Write them on the dotted lines.

grand _____ _____ _____ _____
brand _____ _____ _____ _____
sand ....

....

....

Blends: { br cr dr gr pr tr fr }

Look at each picture and say the word. Then
use one of the above blends to begin each word.

Now look at the endings below.
Match each ending to the correct picture.

{
idge   anch   og   unk   ass
uit   am   ab   um   own   ip
apes   ick   ap   ay   ee
}

Blends: cr fr gr

Read the words below. Tick the ones which are REAL words. Put a cross by the words which are NOT real words.

crup	frig	grin	crop	from
crab	grig	grab	crip	grip
frock	crack		grob	crat
frost	green		frill	grum

Choose one of the words below to fill in the blanks in the sentences.

croft	frills	grass	cross
crab	frost	grin	grill

1 Last night there was a hard _____.

2 I will be _____ if there is a mess in the lounge.

3 Jane had _____ on her dress.

4 It is better to _____ fish than to fry it.

5 The sand was full of _____s.

6 The boy had a big _____ on his face.

7 The _____ had just been cut.

8 The man lived in a _____ in the glen.

Blends: br pr dr tr

Read the words below. Circle the words which are REAL words. Put a cross by the words which are NOT real words.

brat	prob	drop	trig
drub	pram	bret	trip
prip	brown	drag	trick
drill	brum	prist	trin

Use br pr dr tr to begin each word below.

___am	___ing	___um
___ag	___op	___ick
___ink	___ug	___od
___oom	___amp	___and
___ust	___ess	___unk

Now choose the correct word to complete the sentences below.

1 Don't [prop / drop] the [tricks / bricks] on my foot!

2 An elephant can use its [drunk / trunk] to [drink. / brink.]

3 After washing the [press, / dress,] you must [dress / press] it.

Blends: cr dr tr

Blend the sounds below to make words beginning with cr dr **and** tr .
The lines will tell you how many words you can make with each blend.

cr		b	<u>cr</u>	<u>dr</u>	<u>tr</u>
cr	a		_____	_____	_____
		g	_____	_____	_____
dr	i		_____	_____	_____
		ck	_____		_____
tr	u		_____		_____
		m			

Vocabulary Quiz

(Use words from the exercise above.)

cr **words: Which one means...?**

1   To force into or stuff down.   _____

2   A painful stiffness of neck muscles,
    sometimes caused by a sudden movement.   _____

3   A sudden sharp noise; a split or break.   _____

dr **words: Which one means...?**

1   A chemical substance used in medicine
    but sometimes taken illegally.   _____

2   To pull something heavy.   _____

3   Dull, dreary, colourless.   _____

tr **words: Which one means...?**

1   To make neat or tidy by cutting (such as hair).   _____

2   A strong vehicle to carry goods (a small lorry).   _____

3   A type of bus which moves along tracks.   _____

Blends: | gr | br | fr | pr |

Make 8 words beginning with | gr | and | br | from the table below.

(The vowel 'i' has a long sound in one of the 'gr' words.)

		m
gr		
	a	g
	i	nd
br		
		ck

_____   _____

_____   _____

_____   _____

_____   _____

Which of the words you have found mean...?

1   To boast.   _____

2   A metric unit of weight.   _____

3   Edge (for example, of a cup or hat).   _____

4   Goods of particular make or trade mark.   _____

Make 6 words beginning with | fr | and | pr | from the table below.

		m
fr	a	
		p
	o	
		g
pr	i	
		nt

_____   _____

_____   _____

_____   _____

Now use each of the words you have found to complete the sentences.

1   The washing-line was held up with a clothes _____.

2   The kidnap victim saw his name in big _____ on the _____ page of the newspaper.

3   She bought a new _____ for her baby _____ Mothercare.

4   It is interesting to watch _____s jump about, but I would not like to pick one up!

Blend: thr

Complete each word by putting the initial
blend , reading each word as you do so.

___ill   ___ee   ___ob   ___ust

___ive   ___ice   ___oat   ___ift

___one   ___ong   ___ow   ___ush

___ough   ___ew   ___ash

___eat   ___ead

Now write each word in the correct list.

˘   ─

Short Vowel   **Long Vowel**

_____   _____

_____   _____

_____   _____

_____   _____

_____   _____

_____   _____

_____   _____

_____   _____

_____

Which 2 'thr' words are pronounced
the same but have different spellings?

_____   _____

Blends: fr thr

Choose the correct blend (fr) or (thr) to complete each word.
Four words can be completed with either blend.

___og	___ow	___ee	___agment	___ob
___eeze	___esh	___eat	___iend	___ash
___ill	___ifty	___ont	___ight	___ive
___iction	___ust	___inge	___own	___isk

Choose either (fr) or (thr) to complete
the words in the sentences below.

1   The queen sat on a golden ___one, looking old and rather ___ail.

2   ___ozen food is kept in the ice compartment of a ___idge.

3   She looked for a needle and ___ead to take up the hem of her ___ock.

4   When you have the flu, you ___equently have a sore ___oat and a ___obbing headache.

5   If you do something ___ice, you do it ___ee times.

6   When we looked ___ough the window, we saw a ___ush on the window-sill.

7   The dessert was ___esh ___uit salad with cream.

8   John ___ew the ball so high that ___ank could not catch it.

Blends: cr tr pr scr str spr

Blend the Beginning, Middle and End sounds below to make 5 words beginning with (cr) (tr) and (pr).

cr		p	*crop*	_____
tr	o	d	_____	_____
pr		t		_____

Now use 3 of the words you have made to complete the sentence.

The horse _____ on the farmer's _____ as it started to _____ across the fields.

Blend the Beginning, Middle and End sounds below to make 6 words.

tr			_____	_____
str	i	p		
spr			_____	_____
scr	a	nt	_____	_____

Now match each word you have made to the meanings below.

1 An outing.   _____
2 To run, as in a race.   _____
3 Left-over food or material.   _____
4 To take off all your clothes.   _____
5 Used to catch animals.   _____
6 A narrow band used to fasten things.   _____

Blends: scr str spr

Choose the correct short vowel to finish the words below.

scr__m	str__ng	spr__ng	scr__ff
str__ct	str__t	scr__pt	str__ss
str__tch	str__nd	scr__b	str__ck

Choose the ending to make a REAL word – only ONE ending is correct.

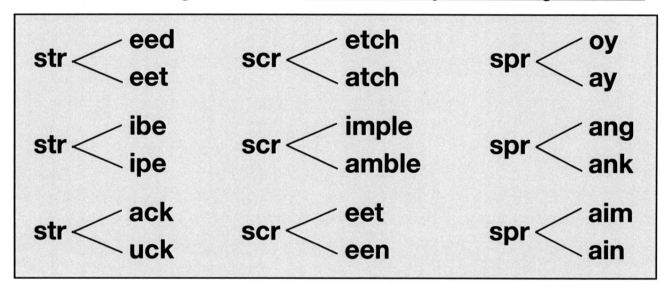

str < eed / eet

scr < etch / atch

spr < oy / ay

str < ibe / ipe

scr < imple / amble

spr < ang / ank

str < ack / uck

scr < eet / een

spr < aim / ain

Complete the sentences below by unscrambling the words in brackets. Each word begins with scr str or spr.

1   The children were told by their _____ (risttc) mother to
_____ (rpsace) the mud off their boots before they came in,
or they would have to _____ (brsuc) the doorstep!

2   The man walked with such big _____s (driste) that his little
son _____d (lgsutrge) to keep up with him.

3   Can you give me some _____ (rgsotn) _____ (isntgr)
to tie up the parcel.

4   The _____ (rirtsnpe) could not finish the race because he
_____ed (rsinpa) his ankle.

5   Tracy _____ed (csertth) out her hand to _____ (etksor)
the little _____ (rtysa) cat which was looking for a home.

Blends: | scr | str | spr |

Choose the correct blend to complete each word.
In some cases, more than one blend may be possible.

___aight	___ing	___ain	___atch	___ipt
___ess	___ipe	___int	___ibble	___ape
___etch	___out	___ide	___eech	___aw
___ee	___inkle	___ike	___ub	___ong

Blend each prefix with the second part of the word, which begins with (scr) or (str). You should be able to make 13 words.

con	scribe
in	strict
de	strain
re	struction
sub	script
	struct

con_____   in_____
con_____   in_____
con_____   in_____
con_____   de_____
con_____   de_____
sub_____   re_____
                re_____

Now use some of these words to complete the sentences.
(The first syllable of the word has been given.)

1 The army con_____s were given in_____ in how to load a gun.

2 You can feel very con_____ed wearing a seat-belt.

3 The con_____ of the building was so complicated that it was difficult to de_____ it.

4 The policeman tried to re_____ the drunk man who was behaving in a violent manner.

5 I sub_____ to the National Geographic magazine.

Blend: shr

Put a short vowel in to the (shr) words below.

shr__nk	**shr__d** **shr__ll** **shr__b**
shr__mp	**shr__g** **shr__vel**

**Use three of the above words to write
sentences of your own on the lines below.**

_____

_____

_____

_____

_____

Now use the (shr) words below to complete the sentences.

**shrew   shrewd   shriek   shrine
shroud   shrapnel**

1   When the bomb exploded, many people were injured
     by _____.

2   A _____ is a holy or sacred place where pilgrims go.

3   The girl gave a loud _____ when she saw the snake.

4   A tiny _____ was spotted on the river bank.

5   Dead bodies are sometimes wrapped in a _____.

6   A _____ person is intelligent, and judges people and
     situations well.

Blends: thr shr

Complete each word below by choosing (thr) or (shr).
Two words can be completed with either blend.

___ank	___ee	___ash	___oud	___ifty
___ough	___ed	___ow	___ill	___ead
___ine	___ew	___ub	___eat	___ug

Which 2 words from the above exercise
have the same sound but are spelt differently?

(Write the words here.) _____   _____

Now use each word to fill in the blanks in the sentence below.

Tom _____ the ball _____ the window.

Choose the ending to make a REAL word – only ONE ending is correct.

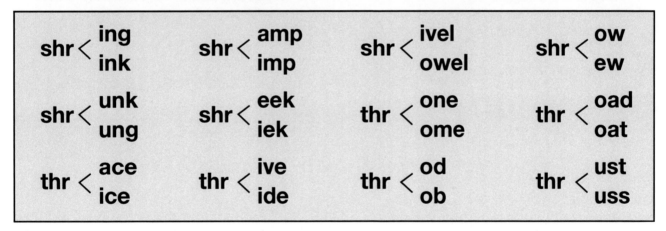

Now choose (thr) or (shr) to complete the words in the sentences.

1   It was such a ___ill to ride on the big wheel that the children ___ieked with excitement.

2   The woman tore the note into ___eds and ___ust the pieces into her pocket.

3   The boy ___ugged his shoulders when he was asked what kind of person sits on a ___one.

Blends:  gl pl sl

**Join the beginning of each word with the
correct ending. Then write out each word.**

gl	ap	1 _glass_
pl	ad	2 _____
sl	uck	3 _____
gl	od	4 _____
pl	ass	5 _____
sl	an	6 _____
pl	ing	7 _____
sl	im	8 _____

Fill in the missing short vowel in the words below.

ă ĕ ĭ ŏ ŭ

pl__m	gl__d	pl__g	sl__g
pl__n	sl__p	pl__mp	sl__m
gl__ss	sl__sh	pl__nk	sl__ck

Blends: gl pl sl

Join the beginning of each word with the correct ending. Then write each word on the lines provided.

gl	uck	1 _____
pl	ime	2 _____
sl	ance	3 _____
gl	under	4 _____
pl	eep	5 _____
sl	unge	6 _____
gl	ouch	7 _____
pl	itter	8 _____
sl	oomy	9 _____

Fill in the missing short vowel in the words below.

pl__nty   sl__ther   gl__ss   pl__net

sl__ng   pl__stic   pl__ump   sl__nder

gl__nd   pl__dge   gl__mmer   sl__t

Choose (ee) (ea) (ai) or (oa) to complete the words below.

gl___m   pl___t   sl___t   gl___t

pl___n   gl___   sl___n   pl___

Blends: 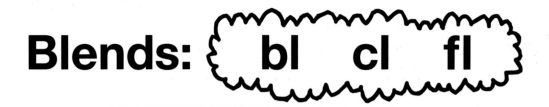 bl cl fl

Read the words below. Circle the ones which are REAL
words. Put a cross by the words which are NOT real words.

block	**clob**	**flig**	**blot**
flat	**blish**	**clap**	**flag**
clut	**flump**	**blank**	**blib**
fling	**clock**	**cliff**	**flod**

Now put each of the words below in the correct sentence.

blunt   cloth   flat   blink   fluffy

1   The land was very _____. There were no hills.

2   She put the wet _____ in the bucket.

3   The rabbit felt soft and _____.

4   It is not good to write with a _____ pencil.

5   If you look at the sun it can make you _____.

Blends: | bl | cl | fl |

Read the words below. Circle the ones which are REAL words. Put a cross by the words which are NOT real words.

clook	blister	flannel	blint	classic
flex	client	blump	fluent	clime
blossom	flane	blew	fluke	clumsy
blob	flute	climp	blaze	flisk
clutch	blave	flinch	flave	blend

Now put each of the words below in the correct sentence.

bland   climate   flute   climax
blemish   clarinet   fluid   blurt
flicker   blatant   flimsy

1 It is not a very good idea to wear _____ clothing in a very cold _____.

2 The child _____ed out the truth because he could not keep his guilty secret any longer.

3 The gifted musician could play both the _____ and the _____ to a very high standard.

4 The _____ of the play was when the hero was killed.

5 The baby's skin was soft and smooth, completely without _____.

6 If you have flu, you should drink plenty of _____s.

7 Not a _____ of shame or embarrassment crossed the boy's face as he told the _____ lie.

8 Plain food without spices can be described as _____.

Blends: gl sl bl cl fl pl

Visual Discrimination

Look carefully to find the word in the box hidden in the line of letters. The number tells you how many times the word is hidden.

glad	b l a b g l a b g l a d l a d g a	1
slip	s l i b s l i p s i l p s l i p l	2
blue	d b l u e d b l u e d l u b l u e	3
clip	c l i d i b c i l p c l i p i p i	1
flag	t f l a g f l a g l f l a f l a g	3
play	b l a y l p a y p l a y p l a y a	2
slab	s l a p s l a d s l a b d s a l b	1
blob	o b l o b b l o b d b d b l o b d	3
bled	b e l d b l e d b l e d l e b e d	2
plug	p l a g p l u g p l u g l p l u g	3
slid	s i l d s l i d s l i b s l i d s	2
cling	c i l n g c i n g c l i n g c l i	1
glib	g l i b g i l b g l i d g l i b l	2
blind	b l i n b l i d b l i n b l i n d	1
clam	c a l m c l a m c l a n c l a m p	2

Rhyming Words:  gl sl bl cl fl pl

In each line of letters find ONE word which rhymes with the word inside the box. The word you are looking for must begin with an 'l' blend.

glum	u b l u m p u l m u g p l u m p
slip	a f i l p i c l i p g l i p i l
black	a s a l c k b l a n k s l a c k
fling	s i l n g c l i n g l i n g i n
clock	a b o l c k o c k o g f l o c k
plan	s l a m c a l n f l a n c l a m
glass	c a l s s c l a s s g l o s s o
slap	f l a p c a l p p l a p f l o p
blush	s h u g l u s h u h s l u s h u
plot	o f l o t b o l t b l o t o p l

Write the rhyming pairs on the lines below. Can you think of one more word to rhyme with each pair? Write it on the dotted line as in the example.

glum _____ _____ _____ _____

plum _____ _____ _____ _____

hum ------------ ------------ ------------ ------------

_____ _____ _____ _____ _____

_____ _____ _____ _____ _____

------------ ------------ ------------ ------------ ------------

Rhyming Words:  gl sl bl cl fl pl

In each line of letters find ONE word which rhymes with the word inside the box. The word you are looking for must begin with an 'l' blend.

glide	s i l d s l i d e d i d e b i g
slick	b i c k s i l k i k c l i c k i
glade	e b l a d e p l a b e s a l d e
clump	s u l m p l u m b p l u m p l u
flame	d b l a m e f l a m b l a n e f
blow	s l s l w l b g l o w c l a w r
slight	h i g h f l i g h t s l i h g t
flint	i g l i n t g l i t n s l i n t
pleat	c l e a n t f l a t e b l e a t
clay	e b a p l a y s a l y b l a y u

Write 5 rhyming pairs on the lines below. Can you think of other rhyming words for each pair? Write them on the dotted line as in the example.

glide _____ _____ _____ _____
slide _____ _____ _____ _____
hide ·········· ·········· ·········· ··········

·········· ·········· ·········· ·········· ··········

·········· ·········· ·········· ·········· ··········

Blends: { gl sl bl cl fl pl }

**Look at each picture and say the word. Then
use ONE of the above blends to begin each word.**

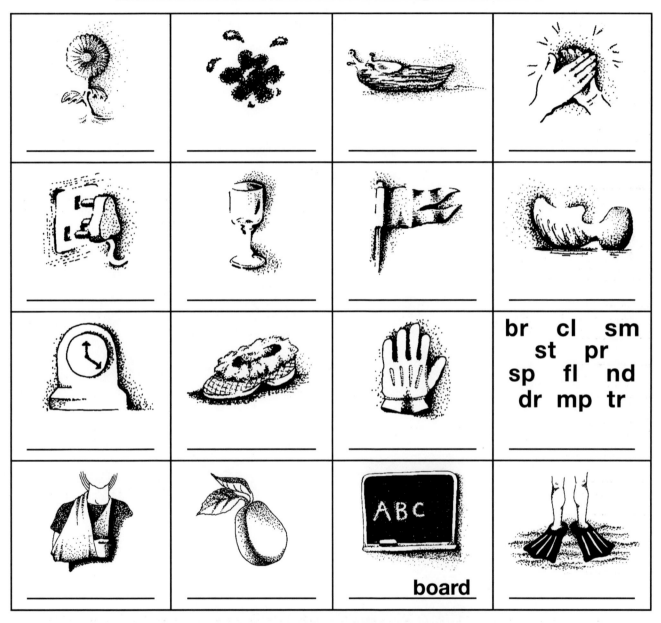

_____	_____	_____	_____
_____	_____	_____	_____
_____	_____	_____	br cl sm st pr sp fl nd dr mp tr
_____	_____	board	_____

**Now look at the endings below.
Match each ending to the correct picture.**

ag	ock	ipper	ack	ing
ug	ass	ippers	ower	ends	ove
og	ot	ug	ap	um

49

Blends: gl sl bl cl fl pl

Read the words below. Circle the ones which are REAL words. Put a cross by the words which are NOT real words.

glad	flob	flap	clam	plig
clag	plum	slim	slant	clog
slimp	blod	plop	slib	clan
flip	blam	glim	bled	fling

Choose the correct blend to make a REAL word.

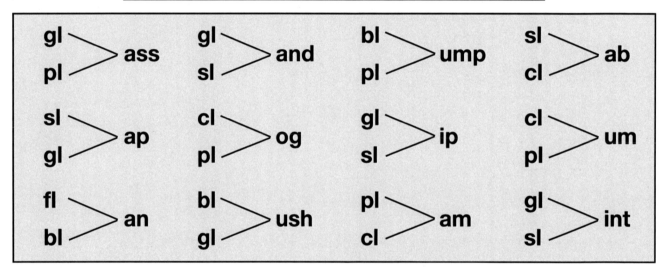

Now choose the correct blend to finish the words in the sentences.

1   There was a ___ack ink ___ob on the ___ean table ___oth.

2   Sally ___ept very well under her nest of thick ___ankets.

3   Jane broke her arm, and had to use a ___ing while it was in __aster.

4   For Christmas, Rachel got a pair of ___uffy ___ippers and some wool ___oves.

5   Tim lived on the top ___oor of a tall ___ock of ___ats, so he was ___ad that there was a lift.

6   Alice had to wear a white ___ouse and ___ack skirt to school, but at home she always wore ___ue jeans.

7   For lunch she ate some cheese ___an and a thick ___ab of fruit cake, and she drank a ___ass of cold milk.

Blends: gl bl sl fl

Blend the Beginning, Middle and End sounds in the exercises below to make as many words as possible.

B	M	E
		d
	a	ss
gl		n
	e	m
bl	o	nd

_____   _____

_____   _____

_____   _____

_____   _____

_____   _____

Now use some of the words to fill in the blanks in the sentences.

1 Hannah had long _____y black hair, but her sister had short _____ hair.

2 Jo stood on a splinter of _____, so his foot _____ badly.

B	M	E
		ck
	a	
sl		p
	i	
fl		sh
	o	ng

_____   _____

_____   _____

_____   _____

_____   _____

_____   _____

_____   _____

_____   _____

1 The _____ of lightning lit up the _____ of sheep on the hill.

2 "Don't _____ on the wet floor!" said Mrs. Bunting to her husband. "Your arm is already in a _____!"

3 The kitten escaped because the cat-_____ was left open.

Blends:  cl pl

**In this exercise you have to use ALL the possible
words to fill in the blanks in the sentences below.**

B	M	E
		m
	a	
cl		p
	o	
pl		nk
	u	mp

_____   _____

_____   _____

_____   _____

_____   _____

_____   _____

_____

1   The pebble fell into the water with a small _____.

2   Mussels and _____s are types of shellfish.

3   Cheap wine is sometimes called _____.

4   The land was dry and bare except for a few _____s
    of rough grass.

5   The _____ pudding tasted very nice, but it made
    Sally feel full up.

6   The clip-_____ of horses' hooves rang out clearly
    in the still night air.

7   There was a loud _____ing sound as the wheels of
    the car on the double yellow lines were _____ed.

8   The crew started to _____ when the
    _____ couple wobbled their way along the
    narrow gang-_____ to board the ship!

Blend: spl

Find 10 words beginning with (spl) in the wordsearch.
Then match each word to the definitions below.
(Words go ACROSS and DOWN only.)

i	s	f	m	d	k	h	n	s
s	p	l	i	n	t	e	r	p
p	l	s	p	l	e	e	n	l
l	u	p	q	a	s	j	o	e
e	t	l	e	l	p	b	r	n
n	t	a	s	p	l	a	y	d
d	e	s	p	l	i	c	e	o
i	r	h	t	g	n	c	v	u
d	s	p	l	i	t	w	y	r

1 A support for a broken bone. _ _ _ _ _ _

2 To break into parts. _ _ _ _ _

3 Great brightness or magnificence. _ _ _ _ _ _ _ _ _

4 To speak quickly and in a confused
   way because of excitement, or fear... _ _ _ _ _ _ _ _

5 Internal organ of the human body. _ _ _ _ _ _

6 What you make when you jump in a
   swimming pool. _ _ _ _ _ _

7 Wonderful, magnificent. _ _ _ _ _ _ _ _

8 To join two ends of a rope or string by
   untwisting and interweaving the strands in it. _ _ _ _ _ _

9 Sharp and thin fragment of wood which
   has broken off from the main piece. _ _ _ _ _ _ _ _

10 To make opposite sides of an
   opening diverge. _ _ _ _ _ _

53

Mixed Blends: { gr/gl bl/br cl/cr }

Choose (gr) or (gl) to finish each word below.

___een	___ad	___id	___ace	___eam
___ide	___itter	___ape	___ope	___ue
	___oat		___ound	

Choose (bl) or (br) to finish each word below.

___ing	___ank	___ess	___ace	___im
___ister	___ock	___oth	___ot	___ick
	___emish		___eeze	

Choose (cl) or (cr) to finish each word below.

___ang	___ot	___ib	___ush	___atter
___est	___ave	___aw	___ear	___ess
	___ench		___ook	

**In the box below, circle the 4 endings which can go
with BOTH initial blends to make a REAL word.**

For example: | gr<u>ade</u> / gl<u>ade</u> |

Then complete the remaining words with the correct blend.

gr/gl	bl/br	cl/cr
__im	__and	__aim
(__ade)	__ack	__amp
__ide	__ag	__ab
__ance	__each	__ash
__and	__eed	__ane
__oom	__end	__ean
__ub	__ain	__ate
__ass	__ink	__own
__ave	__ame	__ick
__int	__idge	__ing

Mixed Blends:  fl/fr pl/pr

Choose (fl) or (fr) to finish each word below.

___og	___et	___abby	___ick	___isk
___ing	___oat	___ower	___inge	___uit
	___uff		___illy	

Choose (pl) or (pr) to finish each word below.

___ess	___ain	___ant	___ime	___une
___onk	___ump	___each	___under	___ince
	___ate		___im	

In the boxes below, circle the 4 endings which can go with BOTH initial blends to make a REAL word.

For example: | **fl**ame / **fr**ame |

Then complete the remaining words with the correct blend.

fl/fr		pl/pr	
__at	__ake	__od	__ice
(__ame)	__om	__ace	__ay
__eak	__ight	__am	__ug
__ock	__ee	__op	__y
__idge	__icker	__edge	__ize

Choose 'l' or 'r' to complete the words in the sentences below.

1   Would you like to f__y to F__ance at a high p__ice, or
    would you p__efer to go by ferry if you are af__aid of flying?

2   The p__ank was made of p__ywood.

3   F__ank got the f__ight of his life when he saw three
    bank robbers f__eeing f__om the bank with shotguns.

TEACHING NOTES AND GUIDELINES

Worksheet 1   st   sp   Level One

Make sure the pupil can distinguish each sound before beginning the worksheet by giving a quick sound discrimination exercise. These sounds are similar enough to cause confusion. The sound /sp/ can be mistaken for /sb/ by pupils who have difficulty distinguishing the voiced /b/ and the voiceless /p/. Pupils who display this sort of confusion should be told explicitly that the blend 'sb' does not exist in the English spelling system. The blend 'st' is a very important one in that it is found at the end of many words as well as at the beginning. (See *"Spotlight on Blends", Book Two,* for worksheets on 'st' in final position.) As suggested in the general introduction, the use of coloured pens is recommended to highlight each blend. This applies to all worksheets in the book in which one blend is contrasted with another.

The vocabulary in this worksheet is simple and only uses short vowels, although a few longer words are used in the sentence completion exercise. As only some of the target words are used in the gap-filling exercise, more able pupils can be encouraged to write sentences of their own with some of the remaining words.

Worksheet 2   st   sp   Level Two

This is the same format as for Worksheet 1, but uses a higher level of vocabulary. Some of the target words contain long vowels or have two syllables, so more advanced spelling knowledge is required. A higher reading level is also assumed for the gap-filling exercise, and sentences 5 and 6 have two missing words which automatically makes the task more difficult. In the last sentence, pupils could be asked to look for three words other than the target words which contain the blend 'st', namely *'best', 'stood'* and *'started'.*

As a follow-up, pupils could be asked to spell words used in the last exercise without looking at the worksheet. Other words for spelling could include: *'speak', 'spike', 'spirit', 'spy', 'starch', 'stock', 'steam', 'start', 'state(ment)', 'static'.*

Worksheet 3   sm   sn   Level One

These two blends involve the nasal sounds /m/ and /n/ and are similar enough to cause confusion for pupils with poor sound processing skills. However, the different position of lips and tongue in pronouncing each blend can be demonstrated easily, with a mirror if necessary. The target words for spelling involve short vowel sounds only, and include words ending in 'sh', 'ff', 'll' and 'ck'. The wordsearch activity is a visual discrimination task, and gives the pupil practice in writing each word out. The eight words can be used for alphabet sequencing practice as a follow-up. The words used in the sentence reading exercise contain long vowel choices. Although the pupil may not have reached these choices on the spelling programme s/he is following, it is assumed that s/he can read words such as *'snail', 'snake',* and *'smile'.*

Worksheet 4   sm   sn   Level Two

The first exercise is similar to that in Worksheet 3, but in some cases both endings can be used to make words, for example, *'smell' / 'smelt'*. The target words include some with long vowel sounds and one two-syllable word, *'snooker'*.

Pupils might not be familiar with all the vocabulary, such as *'smug', 'smock'* (which could be mis-read as *'smoke'*), and *'snag'* and *'snort'*. Some dictionary work might thus be appropriate, or help given where necessary so that the pupil writes down the correct total of words as requested in the instructions.

For the sentence reading exercise, give the pupil credit if s/he manages to combine two of the target words in one sentence. If the pupil is not familiar with all the target words for exercise one, encourage him/her to use one or two of the new words which s/he has learnt.

Some harder words are introduced in the last exercise for word recognition only. If the pupil can read the word without hesitation, s/he can tick it. Once the words have all been ticked, the pupil can be asked to recall the words without looking at the sheet as an optional memory exercise.

Worksheet 5   st   sp   sn   sm   Level One

The reading of nonsense words requires the pupil to decode phonologically without the aid of visual recall. Younger pupils quite like the idea of putting 'nonsense' or 'rubbish' words in the bin, but ensure they know what is meant by a nonsense word before doing the worksheet. This format can be adapted for any spelling pattern, and teachers might like to make up their own worksheets based on the same idea. Pupils should be encouraged to say the nonsense word aloud and write it out from memory, blending the sounds together. S/he should then check that it is correct.

The sentence reading exercise involves choosing the correct blend. The pupil should now be familiar with most of the target words. The last sentence is slightly harder as the incomplete words are next to each other. However, it should be fairly obvious that the first incomplete word is *'stop'*. The second word is easily deduced from the context.

Worksheet 6   st   sp   sn   sm   Level Two

The first exercise is similar to that in Worksheet 5, only the words include those with long and short vowels, and two-syllable words to practise syllable division.

The sentence reading exercise assumes a higher level of vocabulary, but context should make it clear what initial blend to use. The words *'smirk'* and *'snigger'* are less common (sentence number 4) but the sentence itself provides a suitable definition of each word.

For those who have little experience of walking in the countryside, the word *'stile'* might also be unfamiliar! Ensure that the pupil knows the difference between the homophones *'style'* and *'stile'*.

Two or three of the sentences could be given for dictation as an optional follow-up to the worksheet.

Worksheets 7a & b   sk   sc   Level Two

Most pupils should not have any difficulty in distinguishing this sound at the beginning of words, although the blends 'sc' or 'sk' sound very similar to /sg/ in certain conditions. If a pupil confuses the sounds /k/ and /g/, he or she should be told that the letter 's' can blend with 'c' or 'k' but never with 'g'.

The purpose of Worksheets 7a and 7b is to give practice of the rule concerning whether to use 'sc' or 'sk' at the beginning of words and syllables. Pupils who are following a structured spelling programme should already be familiar with the rule about 'c' and 'k' at the beginning of words, namely that initial hard /k/ sound is spelt with a 'c' when followed by vowels 'a', 'o' or 'u', and with a 'k' when followed by vowels 'e' and 'i'. This basic rule also applies with the blends 'sc' and 'sk'. The blend 'sk' is more common at the end of words. (See *"Spotlight on Blends"*, *Book Two*, for a worksheet on 'sk' as an end blend.)

There are only a few words beginning with 'sk' which include rather difficult words such as *'skeleton'* and *'skewer'*. Some of the 'sc' words are also less common. These worksheets are therefore more appropriate for pupils with well developed reading and spelling skills. However, the first exercise in Worksheet 7b can be completed by merely following the rule, while the second exercise is aimed at vocabulary extension, and gives practice in writing out a few of the longer words. The two-syllable words with 'sc' or 'sk' in the middle are included for recognition purposes, and can be used for syllable division work.

It is unfortunate that the exceptions to the rule include two very common 'sk' words – *'skate'* and *'skull'*. Make sure that the pupil knows these words. More artistic pupils might like to illustrate the sentence suggested as a way of remembering the words which are exceptions to the rule.

The use of different colour pens is particularly recommended for this worksheet, including the writing of the correct spelling choices 'sc' or 'sk' in the boxes at the top of Worksheet 7a.

Worksheets 8a & b   squ   squa   Level Two

Pupils should be familiar with 'qu' words before being introduced to the blend 'squ' which is the most difficult of the 's' blends. There are not many words beginning with 'squ' and most of the words in Worksheet 8a should be familiar to pupils. It can be pointed out that three of the words are 'sound' words: *'squeak', 'squeal'* and *'squelch'*. Worksheet 8b focuses on 'squa' words in which the vowel has the sound /ŏ/. This can be linked to 'wa' and 'swa' words such as *'wash, 'swamp'*, etc., where the vowel sound is altered in the same way. The vocabulary level in 8b is higher and pupils might need help with some of the word meanings.

8a

1 squirrel	6 squint
2 squeeze	7 squelch
3 square	8 squeal
4 squeak	9 squiggle
5 squirt	10 squid

8b

Words	Sentences
1 squawk	1 squabble
2 squander	2 squalid
3 squat	3 squall
4 squash	4 squawk
5 squall	5 squander
6 squalid	6 squad
7 squad	7 squash
8 squabble	8 squat

Worksheet 9   sw tw dw   Level Two

This is a fairly straightforward worksheet, although the vocabulary level with words like *'twirl', 'tweak', 'dwindle', 'dwell'*, etc., would make this unsuitable for the younger learner. Most of the words begin with 'sw' or 'tw', as 'dw' is an infrequent blend occurring only in the words given in the worksheet. This should be pointed out to the pupil in case s/he confuses blends 'tw' and 'dw' which are similar in sound.

Worksheet 10   br cr tr   Level One

This is the first of a number of worksheets on 'r' blends. These blends need endless practice because they are not only very common, but frequently cause articulation problems. The blend 'tr', for example, is sometimes pronounced by younger children as /ch/, and may thus be spelt 'ch' instead of 'tr'. Those who have trouble in pronouncing /r/ often articulate the sound as /w/, so the blends 'br', 'cr' and 'tr' may be pronounced, and hence spelt, 'bw', 'cw' and 'tw' respectively.

All the words in the first exercise have short vowels, and there are six nonsense words. Different words are used in the sentence completion exercise, including words which are harder to spell such as *'brown'* and *'brother'*. However, these are all common words which the pupil should be able to read. The last two sentences are more difficult since two words are missing, but only four possible words remain to fill in the blanks, so the choice should be obvious.

Worksheet 11   br   cr   tr   Level Two

This worksheet follows a similar format to number 9, but employs a much greater variety of phonic patterns in the first exercise including words with long vowel sounds and two-syllable words which display different syllable patterns (for example, *'tripod', 'tribute'* and *'brandish'*).

The gap-filling exercise is made more challenging by the deletion of two words in most sentences. Pupils might not know one or two of the words, such as *'brisk'* or *'crude',* so this exercise could also provide an opportunity for vocabulary extension. Make sure that the pupil does not mis-read *'breath'* (short vowel) with *'breathe'* (long vowel), and point out the different patterns as necessary.

Worksheet 12   dr   gr   pr   Level One

The first exercise is an onset-and-rime sound blending task involving simple words with short vowels only, apart form the word *'green'*. There is only one possibility for each beginning and ending except for the ending 'een' which can blend with both 'gr' and 'pr'. However, it is assumed that younger pupils will not know the word *'preen'*.

For the second exercise, more than one short vowel can be used to complete some of the words, for example, *'pram'* or *'prim'*. The word *'gr___b'* is included twice so that the pupil can make both *'grab'* and *'grub'*.

Worksheet 13   dr   gr   pr   Level Two

This worksheet follows the same format as number 12, only the target words for both exercises contain both long and short vowels, and use a greater variety of phonic patterns. Four of the words in the second exercise can be completed by more than one vowel choice. These choices are as follows: *'drill' / 'droll'* ; *'gram' / 'grim'* ; *'draft' / 'drift'* ; and *'grape' / 'gripe' / 'grope'*.

Worksheet 14   br   dr   Level One

Visual Discrimination Practice Sheet

This worksheet is a Visual Discrimination Exercise on 'br' and 'dr' designed for pupils who confuse 'b' and 'd'. Pupils can use a highlighter to find the hidden words, or circle around them with a coloured pen.

Worksheet 15   fr   Level One

This blend is not contrasted in this introductory worksheet as it is one which presents more articulation difficulties than the other 'r' blends, especially for pupils who confuse the sound /f/ with /th/ as in *'thin'*.

The words selected for this worksheet are the most common ones beginning with 'fr', although *'frail'* and *'frank'* might not be known by younger pupils.

This worksheet is a departure from the normal sound blending exercises and it involves the solving of anagrams. Pupils should be encouraged to look for logical letter combinations when unscrambling the words given. The suggested memory exercise is an optional extra.

A worksheet like this also lends itself to more advanced alphabet sequencing work. Sound blending practice of 'fr' words is given in subsequent worksheets with mixed 'r' blends.

Worksheet 16   fr   Level Two

This is a far more challenging worksheet on 'fr' as it employs a more advanced vocabulary, and the questions are designed to test both grammatical knowledge and familiarity with syllable structure in longer words.

This type of worksheet has been found very useful with secondary aged pupils or adult learners who are in the later stages of a structured spelling programme, and have more linguistic awareness in general.

Worksheet 17   Mixed 'r' blends   Level One
Rhyming Practice

Give some rhyming practice before commencing the worksheet. Point out that the middle and last sound must be the same for the word to rhyme, and that the letter pattern will also be the same.

Tell the pupil to look for an 'r' blend in each line of letters to find the required word. Most examples have at least one distractor, that is, a nonsense word which rhymes with, or is visually similar to, the target word in the box.

The second exercise is a useful follow-up. Encourage the pupil to suggest further rhyming words. These do not have to begin with an 'r' blend.

Worksheet 18   Mixed 'r' blends   Level Two
Rhyming Practice

This is identical in format to the previous worksheet, but the target words include spelling choices for long vowels as well as for short vowels. Thus, in the second exercise, pupils might well suggest words which have a different spelling pattern to the word given, for example, *'blue'* to rhyme with *'crew'*, or *'moan'* to rhyme with *'prone'*. This provides an opportunity to revise spelling choices for long vowels.

Worksheet 19   Mixed 'r' blends   Level One

This worksheet brings together all the 'r' blends in an exercise which requires the pupil to match the correct blend to each picture. The pupil should then complete each word by selecting the correct ending from the list below the pictures.

Younger pupils might need some help with this exercise as they might not be familiar with patterns such as 'idge' or 'own'. The word *'fruit'* is irregular, but it has been included as it is of high frequency.

There is another approach to this worksheet which is first to write each word on to a card. For example, write *'crown', 'pram', 'tree',* and so on. Then ask the child to read each word, drawing attention to the initial 'r' blend. Following this, the cards can be cut into two pieces to create a jigsaw effect. The 'r' blend should be on one of the pieces, and therefore the remainder of the word on the other. The pupil can then re-assemble the words, re-reading each one as the two jigsaw pieces are put together again. In this way, the pupil should be able to complete the worksheet with minimal help from the teacher as s/he will already have become familiar with the words concerned.

Worksheet 20   cr   fr   gr   Level One

The following few worksheets re-introduce all the 'r' blends but in a different combination. This worksheet uses only words with short vowels in the first exercise except for the word *'green'* which should be known by most pupils. In the second exercise, pupils might not be familiar with the word *'croft'* unless they are on the Fuzzbuzz Reading scheme! However, this appears in the last sentence by which time there will only be one word left to fill the blank. Pupils should be asked to guess what *'croft'* means from the context. The inclusion of words like *'croft'* and *'glen'* could provide an opportunity to raise language awareness of varieties of English and dialect words.

Worksheet 21   br   pr   dr   tr   Level One

This worksheet is a complement to the previous one in that it provides practice of the remaining 'r' blends, also at Level One. The four blends contrasted in this worksheet, however, are ones which could cause sound confusions as they are the voiced/voiceless pairs: 'br' and 'pr'; and 'dr' and 'tr'. A quick auditory discrimination exercise on these contrasted sounds might be appropriate before commencing the worksheet. Visual discrimination confusions might also arise with 'br' and 'dr', or 'br' and 'pr' which are similar both auditorily and visually.

The second exercise involves blending onset (that is, the correct initial blend) with rime (the ending), but is more difficult than other similar exercises since there are four blends to choose from. Pupils should be encouraged to try each combination, for example, *'bram'*, *'pram'*, *'dram'* and *'tram'* for the first word. Several words can be completed by more than one blend.

If this worksheet is being done by more than one pupil, an element of competition could be introduced by awarding bonus points for finding words which can be completed by two or more blends (for example, the words *'brick'*, *'prick'*, *'trick'* would score 3 points).

The third exercise should not present any difficulties as the context makes it clear what words to choose from the alternatives given. These sentences could also be given for dictation as a follow-up.

Worksheet 22   cr dr tr   Level Two

This worksheet involves blending the Beginning, Middle and End sounds to make words beginning with the target blends. The number of lines indicates how many words are possible, and these are as follows: 'cr' words: *'crab'*, *'crack'*, *'cram'*, *'crib'*, *'crick'* (the word *'crag'* is also possible, but is unlikely to be known by most pupils); 'dr' words: *'drab'*, *'drag'*, *'drug'* and *'drum'*; 'tr' words: *'track'*, *'tram'*, *'trick'*, *'trim'* and *'truck'*.

Pupils might also come up with the word *'crum'*, in which case the correct spelling, *'crumb'*, can be linked to words like *'thumb'*, or *'lamb'*. Some pupils might need a little help with the vocabulary exercise, but this can be seen as an opportunity for extending vocabulary by highlighting less common words such as *'crick'* or *'drab'*. It is recognised that many pupils might not know the word *'tram'*, so this can be explained, as necessary.

Worksheet 23   gr br fr pr   Level Two

This worksheet follows much the same format as number 22. The eight words which can be blended in the first exercise are: *'gram'*, *'grand'*, *'grind'* (with long vowel), *'grim'*, *'brag'*, *'brand'*, *'brim'* and *'brick'*. Pupils might not be familiar with one or two of these words, such as *'grim'*, or *'brag'*.

In the second exercise, the six words are: *'from'*, *'frog'*, *'front'* (it will be necessary to point out that the letter 'o' has an /ŭ/ sound in this word), *'pram'*, *'prop'* and *'print'*. Less common words such as *'prig'*, *'prim'* and *'prom'* are also possible, but it is assumed that most pupils will not come up with these words. They can be included in the list if known to the pupils, but, if so, the six target words for the gap-filling exercise should be starred.

Worksheet 24   thr   Level Two

This is not only a difficult sound to distinguish and/or articulate, but words beginning with this blend include several patterns which would normally be taught in the more advanced stages of a spelling programme, for example, 'ew' as in *'threw'*, and 'ea' with the short sound as in *'threat'*. Conversely, some of the 'thr' words which display simpler spelling patterns are words not in common usage such as *'throng'*, *'thrift'* or *'thrive'*. The most common word, and one which the pupil should be encouraged to learn permanently, is the most irregular – *'through'*!

With these considerations, this worksheet only requires the pupil to read each word accurately, and assign it to the correct list according to the vowel sound. Attention is drawn to the homophones *'through'* and *'threw'*.

Worksheet 25   fr   thr   Level Two

This worksheet should only be given after 'fr' and 'thr' have been practised separately. For those pupils who have difficulty with the basic /f/ and /th/ distinction, this worksheet will prove quite demanding. When doing the first exercise, remind the pupil that 'ow' can have two sounds. The four endings which can blend with both 'fr' and 'thr' are: 'ee', 'esh', 'ill' and 'own'. (The vowel sounds in *'frown'* and *'thrown'* are, of course, different although they use the same spelling pattern.)

Worksheet 26   scr str spr   Level One

This worksheet introduces the difficult three-consonant blends 'scr', 'str' and 'spr' by giving initial sound blending practice of related 'cr', 'tr' and 'pr'. The sound blending exercise involving the three-consonant blends is designed to be simple and straightforward, with only two possible short vowels and two endings to choose from.

This worksheet aims at a brief introduction to these difficult three-consonant blends. The following two worksheets provide more detailed practice at a higher level. Some further one-syllable words which might be usefully introduced at this stage if the teacher wishes are: *'string'*, *'strong'*, *'struck'*, *'spring'*, *'scrub'* and *'scrum'*.

Worksheet 27   scr str spr   Level Two

It is assumed that some introductory work has already been done on these difficult three-consonant blends. A brief auditory discrimination exercise is strongly recommended before beginning the worksheet. The first exercise involves choosing the correct short vowel to complete the words, all of which are of one syllable. There are also two difficult end blends in the words *'strict'* and *'script'*. After completing all the words, pupils should go back and re-read each word, aiming for immediate word recognition.

The second exercise is a standard onset-and-rime sound blending task, using a mixture of words with both long and short vowels.

The third exercise presents more of a challenge, and should be viewed as a problem solving activity. Encourage pupils to cross off the three letters which make the initial blend. This should make it easier to unscramble the remaining letters.

Some words such as *'strict'* and *'scrape'* in sentence 1; *'sprinter'* in number 4; and *'stretch'* in number 5, have a combination of letters which would allow two initial blends, for example, 'str' or 'scr' in the anagram *'risttc'* for *'strict'* in the first sentence. For these words, it might avoid frustration to supply pupils with the initial blend.

As far as possible, encourage the pupil to use logic and reasoning to work out sensible letter patterns, and to use context as an additional clue.

The answers to the anagrams are as follows:

1	strict	scrape	scrub
2	stride	struggle	
3	strong	string	
4	sprinter	sprain	
5	stretch	stroke	stray

Worksheet 28   scr str spr   Level Two

This worksheet gives further contrastive practice of the blends 'scr', 'str' and 'spr'. The words in the first exercise are the more common words. They all display regular phonic patterns.

The second exercise involves a higher level of vocabulary and it also assumes a more sophisticated knowledge of word structure. This would make a useful dictionary exercise, as it is likely that many pupils will be unsure about one or two of the possible words.

The consonant sounds in some words are also difficult both to distinguish and articulate, for example, *'constrict'* and *'conscript'*. However, older pupils with a good vocabulary should enjoy the challenge of this exercise.

Worksheet 29   shr   Level Two

This worksheet gives separate practice of 'shr', a difficult blend to pronounce. The easier words are contained in the fist exercise. (There are three short vowels for the first item to give *'shrink'*, *'shrank'* or *'shrunk'*. Point out the similarity to *'drink'*.) If the pupil decides to use *'shrivel'* in a sentence, point out that it is necessary to double the 'l' when adding 'ing' or 'ed' suffix endings (similar to *'travel'*, *'marvel'*, and so on). Harder 'shr' words are contained in the second exercise. The gap-filling exercise is straightforward as only one target word is missing from each sentence, but pupils might need some help if they are unfamiliar with the vocabulary.

Worksheet 30   thr shr   Level Two

It is assumed that both 'shr' and 'thr' will have been practised separately prior to this worksheet which contrasts both blends. (See Worksheets 24 and 29.) This will therefore provide consolidation for both these blends which are difficult to pronounce and hence spell. The two endings which can be completed with either blend in the first exercise are 'ill' and 'ew'.

Attention is once again drawn to the homophones: *'through'* and *'threw'*.

Worksheet 31   gl pl sl   Level One

This is the first of a series of worksheets on 'l' blends. These blends are also very frequent, but present fewer problems with articulation than the 'r' blends. Like the worksheets on the 'r' blends, the 'l' blends are first introduced in groups of three before being contrasted altogether. The three-consonant blend 'spl' is dealt with separately.

The first exercise in this worksheet is a straightforward onset-and-rhyme blending exercise identical in format to Worksheet number 12. Only words with short vowels are used. In the second exercise, more than one short vowel can be used to complete a few of the words, such as *'slog' / 'slug'* ; *'slap' / 'slip'*, and so on.

Worksheet 32   gl pl sl   Level Two

This worksheet practises the same blends as in Worksheet number 31 and follows the same format. However, the target words in the first exercise include a wider variety of phonic patterns. The last exercise is more demanding as it assumes familiarity with alternative spelling choices for long vowels, and the words to be completed include less familiar vocabulary such as *'glee'* or *'slain'*. As there are only a few words to be completed, however, the pupil could be encouraged to use a spell-checker or dictionary to check those s/he is less sure of. If more than one pupil is doing this worksheet, this can be done competitively.

Worksheet 33   bl cl fl   Level One

This is a very straightforward worksheet on the remaining three 'l' blends which is identical in format to Worksheet 10. Most younger pupils should be able to complete this worksheet with minimal help from the teacher, although the words in the first exercise should be read aloud to ensure the pupil is decoding the sounds correctly.

Worksheet 34   bl   cl   fl   Level Two

This worksheet follows the same format as number 33, only employs a greater variety of phonic patterns and a higher level of vocabulary. Several words which begin with an open syllable appear in this worksheet, for example, *'fluent', 'client', 'climate', 'climax'* and *'blatant',* so this is an opportunity to consolidate words of this syllable structure. The vocabulary exercise is designed to extend knowledge of word meanings by the deliberate inclusion of less common words. Some help might therefore be needed for this exercise.

Worksheet 35   Mixed 'l' blends   Level One
Visual Discrimination Practice Sheet

This worksheet is identical in format to number 14 and requires the pupil to find the target words beginning with an 'l' blend hidden in the line of letters. This sort of tracking exercise is useful for dyslexic pupils who frequently display visual sequencing difficulties with words containing the letter 'l', reading words such as *'calm'* as *'clam',* and so on. In each line of letters there are one or more distractors, that is, letter sequences which are similar to the target word such as *'slip'.* Encourage pupils to read and spell each target word aloud prior to tracking, and to name the letters as s/he tracks along the line.

Worksheet 36   Mixed 'l' blends   Level One
Rhyming Practice

This worksheet and the next are identical in format to Worksheets 17 and 18 containing mixed 'r' blends, and the same guidelines apply. The target words are all simple, one-syllable words, although the word *'glum'* might not be known by younger pupils. Stress that the rhyming word hidden in each line of letters must begin with an 'l' blend, which limits the available choices. However, there is at least one distractor in each line of letters, that is, a nonsense word beginning with an 'l' blend which rhymes with the target word, or a real word which is visually similar to the target word.

Worksheet 37   Mixed 'l' blends   Level Two
Rhyming Practice

This follows the same format as number 36, but the target words include words with long vowels. The follow-up exercise allows the teacher to focus on five patterns of his/her choice rather than requiring the pupil to think of further rhyming words for all the rhyming pairs on the sheet, as in number 36.

Worksheet 38   Mixed 'l' blends   Level One

This worksheet follows the same format as number 19, and the same guidelines apply, including the suggestion of doing a jigsaw exercise with the target words on card prior to doing the actual worksheet. The word endings include both 'ipper' and 'ippers', which is a good opportunity to draw attention to the suffix 's'. The 'ove' ending could easily be read with a long vowel sound, but it is part of the word 'glove', an example of the letter 'o' making the short /ŭ/ sound. Pupils in the early stages of reading might need help with decoding the endings 'ipper(s)', 'ove' and 'ower'.

Worksheet 39   Mixed 'l' blends   Level Two

This should provide useful consolidation for 'l' blends for pupils who are already familiar with them, and have had some initial practice.

The first two exercises involve words with short vowels only, and are straightforward sound blending tasks. The sentence completion exercise is obviously more difficult since there are six initial blends to choose from. Hopefully, there is enough contextual information to make the choice obvious in most cases, although the pupil should be encouraged to read the complete sentence before attempting to supply the missing blends.

For pupils who cannot cope with this level of difficulty, the correct sentences can be read aloud by the teacher, enabling the pupil to complete each word from memory. In this case, the pupil should listen to the sentence and repeat it aloud before completing the words, following the same multi-sensory routine as for spelling or dictation. The completed words for each sentence are:

1	black	blob	clean	cloth
2	slept	blankets		
3	plaster	sling		
4	fluffy	slippers	gloves	
5	floor	block	flats	glad
6	blouse	black	blue	
7	flan	slab	glass	

Worksheets 40a & b   gl/bl   sl/fl   cl/pl   Level Two

These worksheets re-introduce the 'l' blends in contrastive pairs, requiring the pupil to blend the Beginning, Middle and End sounds (denoted by the capital letters B, M and E) to make as many words as possible from a given combination of letters. This requires good sound blending skills. Masking some of the distracting letters with card or paper is recommended.

The exercise on 'cl'/'pl' in Worksheet 40b requires the pupil to make eleven words, all of which are needed to fill in the blanks in the sentences. The answers for each sound blending exercise are given below.

Not all pupils will be familiar with all the possible words. Some help might therefore be needed.

gl/bl	Words:		glad	glass	gland	glen	gloss	
			bland	bled	bless	blend	blond	

	Sentences:	1)	gloss (y)	blond
		2)	glass	bled

sl/fl	Words:		slack	slap	slash	slang	slick
			slip	sling	slop	slosh	flap
			flash	flick	flip	fling	flop

	Sentences:	1)	flash	flock
		2)	slip	sling
		3)	flap	

cl/fl	Words:		clam	clap	clank	clamp	clop	clump
			plank	plop	plonk	plum	plump	

	Sentences:	1)	plop		5)	plum		
		2)	clam		6)	clop		
		3)	plonk		7)	clank	clamp	
		4)	clump		8)	clap	plump	plank

Worksheet 41   spl   Level Two

There are not many words beginning with this three-consonant blend and the majority are brought together in this worksheet. The blend itself can be introduced by linking it with 'pl' which should already be familiar to pupils. The wordsearch task is intended to provide a change from the other worksheets, and will furnish the pupil with a useful list of 'spl' words if s/he succeeds in finding the ten words.

One or two of these words such as *'splice'* and *'splay'* are rather technical, and may not be known by the pupil (or teacher!). Once the list is complete, the pupil can be asked to spell a few of the words without looking at the worksheet. The words to match the meanings are as follows:

---

1) splint	6) splash
2) split	7) splendid
3) splendour	8) splice
4) splutter	9) splinter
5) spleen	10) splay

Worksheets 42a & b gr/gl bl/br cl/cr Level Two
fl/fr pl/pr

For pupils who have already practised 'r' and 'l' blends separately, the final two worksheets provide a chance to contrast pairs of similar sounds such as 'gr' / 'gl', 'bl' / 'br'. These worksheets assume knowledge of a wide variety of phonic patterns, and as such they provide excellent sound blending practice of long and short vowels, vowel digraphs, endings such as 'ce' and 'dge', and so on, as well as the targeted initial blends. The four endings which can go with both initial blends are as follows:

gr/gl	ade	and	oom	ass
bl/br	each	and	eed	ink
cl/cr	amp	ash	own	ick
fl/fr	ame	ock	ight	ee
pl/pr	od	op	ay	y